Presented to

GEMMA SPEIRS

By

DYSART KIRK

JUNIOR CHURCH

SESSION 1991/92

The Spangly Dragon

and other funny poems

Feeling Beastly was first published in 1989
Feeling Peckish was first published in 1991
Can't Get to Sleep was first published in 1990
by Methuen Children's Books
This edition published 1992 by Dean,
Michelin House, 81 Fulham Road, London SW3 6RB
Text and illustrations copyright © Mark Burgess
1989, 1991 and 1990
Printed in Great Britain by The Bath Press

A CIP catalogue record for this book
is available from the British Library

ISBN 0 603 55046 0

MARK BURGESS

The Spangly Dragon
and other funny poems

Illustrated by the author

Containing *Feeling Beastly,*
Feeling Peckish and *Can't Get to Sleep*

DEAN

MARK BURGESS

Feeling Beastly

Animal poems

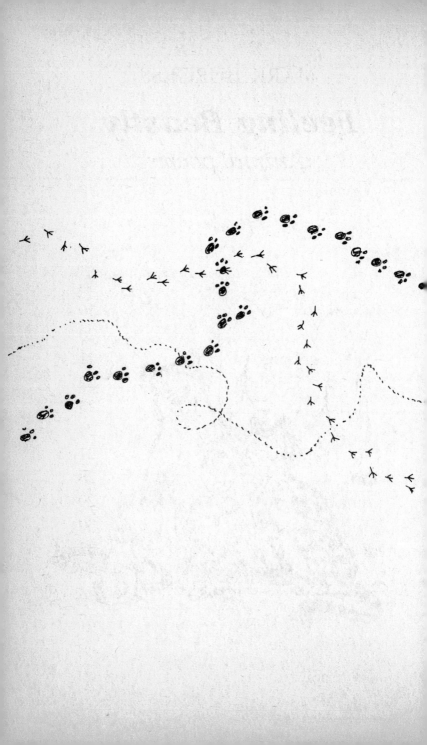

Contents

The Wallaby

A wallaby, whenever it snows,
Suffers from a runny nose.
He keeps on sniffing to try and stop it
And has a hanky in his pocket.

9

Alphabestiary

A was an ass that didn't eat grass,
B was a beautiful bear,
C was a cat, incredibly fat,
And D was a dog with no hair.

E was an elephant, big as a bus,
F was a fidgety fox,
G was a goat, rowing a boat,
And H was a horse in a box.

I was an ibex high in the hills,
J was a jackal with 'flu,
K was a koala, asleep in the parlour,
And L was a louse upon you.

M was a mouse that lived in a house,
N was nothing-at-all,
O was an octopus that came to live with us
And P was a piglet (quite small).

Q was a quail, growing quite frail,
R was a rabbit that *walked*,
S was a snake that made a mistake
And T was the tiger it stalked.

U was an umbrella bird out in the rain,
V was a vegetarian vulture,
And W was a worm, trying to learn
About subterranean culture.

X was an oryx that stood on his head,
Y was a yak in the snow,
And Z was a zebra asleep in a bed,
Dreaming of what? – I don't know.

The Bat

The common flittermouse or bat
Lives inside a paper hat.
At night he flies about the sky
And makes an awful, creaky cry.

He paints his face with carpet glue
Because he likes to look at you,
And if your window he should pass
He'll stick his features to the glass.

Cats

Cats, it's a fact
That everyone knows,
Don't fall on their heads
But land on their toes.
So, why is it, then,
Whenever I'm there,
My cat's by the fire
With his *feet in the air?*

The Kangaroo

Once upon a time I knew
A happy, jolly, kangaroo.
He loved to joke,
He loved to laugh,
He loved to yodel
In the bath.

"Don't be sad,"
He'd say to me,
"Life's such fun
And smiling's free.
Buck up, be brave,
Be hale and hearty –
Come along and join the party!"

Oh, what merriment,
What delight.
We'd dance all day,
We'd dance all night.
The food we had
Was quite superb,
Better music
Never heard.
And when the time
Came round to go,
We'd thank him
For the jolly show.
He'd say, "So glad
That you could come.
Soon we'll have
Another one.
So hop along,
The lot of you,
Cheerio and
Toodle-oo!"

The Slumberglub

Nobody loves the slumberglub,
He's smelly and he stinks.
Nobody loves the slumberglub
(At least, that's what he thinks).
But he doesn't smell so awful –
His scent *delights* the nose.
The slumberglub is unaware
He smells just like a rose.

The Parrot

The parrot's a wonderful bird.
It can imitate speech, I have heard,
But mine will not talk,
Having said, with a squawk,
"Conversing with *you* is absurd."

Adam the Alligator

Adam the alligator,
Whenever he's home,
Talks for hours
On the telephone.
He dials the numbers
With a claw,
And talks from ten
'Til half-past four.
If you try to call *him*
the number's engaged
(So many's the time
I've been enraged).
And now, I've heard
Adam the alligator
Has got engaged
To the 'phone operator.

The Jigsaw Bird

I love to see the jigsaw bird
Flying upside down.
It sings a song that sounds all wrong
And wears a dressing-gown.

I love to see the sawjig bird
Flying downside up.
It feeds on chips and concrete mix
And drinks them from a cup.

Rodney the Rabbit

Rodney the rabbit
Has endless talents.
He's as strong as an ox,
He has excellent balance.

He can put up a shelf,
He can paper a wall,
He can solve any problem
In no time at all.

He can do his own cooking,
He can launder his clothes,
Whatever the question,
The answer he knows.

For Rodney the rabbit
Is terribly clever,
As he'll happily tell you
for ever and ever.

The Wasp

The humble wasp is much maligned,
He really is extremely kind.
Any chap in striped pyjamas
Couldn't really mean to harm us.
It's just he thinks he's still in bed,
Mistakes his tail for his head –
And doesn't mean to use his sting
But only kiss us, silly thing.

Mr and Mrs Fernsey-Howes

Mr and Mrs Fernsey-Howes
Often had domestic rows.
They called each other names and swore.
They wrestled on the kitchen floor.
They tossed the pans, they chucked the china,
The damage done was never minor.
The noise they made was simply frightful.
I never heard of two so spiteful.

That was until one fine Spring day,
For then a tiger came to stay.
He walked up the path, he rang the bell
And (just in case) he knocked as well.
"What do you want?" said Mrs F.
And then she gasped, she caught her breath.
The tiger whispered in her ear:
"Bring in my trunk, now, there's a dear."

25

And then he went straight in to where
Mr F. sat in his chair.
"Now listen," said the earnest cat,
"I make the rules and that is that.
Breakfast at eight, lunch at one,
I like my omelettes under-done."
And when the tiger this had said,
He left the room and went to bed.

No longer do the Fernsey-Howes
Rant and have domestic rows.
No more the sound of kitchen riot;
Their house is peaceful, utter quiet.
The tiger is the perfect gent,
The neighbours think him heaven-sent,
Respected everywhere he goes –
Perhaps he'll soon be mayor, who knows?

The Flamingo

With flamingos, it's not as you'd think –
They're not really meant to be pink.
The Almighty thought blue,
An appropriate hue,
But knocked over his bottle of ink.

Armadillo

An armadillo
When illo
Eats his fillo
And then sleeps
With his head
On a pillow.

Jungle Joke

There's a joke about
That would make you shout –
The piglet giggled at it,
The tamarin grinned,
The crocodile smiled,
The giraffe laughed,
The jackal cackled,
The jackdaw guffawed,
And as for the hyena –
Well, you should have seen her.

The Dinosaurs

The dinosaurs have come to town,
They've come to do their shopping.
They're thrilled to bits – tea at The Ritz
And then they're going bopping.

The Brontosaurus needs a hat,
Triceratops, a coat.
Tyrannos' Rex will sign the cheques
(The rest of them are broke).

The Stegosaurus orders buns,
Diplodocus, currant cake.
The Trachodon bops on and on
And gets a tummy ache.

The dinosaurs are going home,
Their shopping's all been done.
"We had a ball," say one and all,
"Extinction – here we come!"

Rats

To be a rat must be such fun,
I often wish that I was one.
Rats don't have to wash their hands,
They run around in happy bands.
They dance in mud, they play with goo,
No one tells them what to do.
And rats don't have to be polite
Or even go to bed at night!
But life is risky for the rat . . .

. . . Perhaps I'd rather be a *CAT*.

The Crocodile Next Door

A crocodile lives next door,
He's scaly and he's green.
He is the biggest crocodile
That I have ever seen.

He's fierce and terrible that croc',
He has a ghastly grin.
He'll gnash his teeth and likes to think
That you're afraid of him.

But don't be afraid, the horrid beast
Won't think of eating *you*.
Oh, the most disgusting things
Are what he likes to chew.

And he has an awful secret
(Poor beast, it pains him so),
His teeth are only DENTURES.
I'm his dentist – I should know.

Miranda

A girl called Miranda
Sent for a panda.
There arrived at the gate
Not one box but *eight*.
And when she opened them,
What pandamonium!

The Spotted Cow

While walking down a country lane
I met a spotted cow.
The cow, she curtsied daintly,
I answered with a bow.
I doffed my cap, I raised my voice:
"Dear cow, how do you do?"
The cow, she stopped her chewing
And said quite simply, "Moo."

Roberta Hyde

The trouble with Roberta Hyde
Was she was never satisfied.
She'd criticize the whole day long,
Everything was always *WRONG*.
"I don't like this. I don't like that.
I don't want a dog — I want a cat.
This pudding's cold, I want it hot.
I want the things I haven't got!"
Her suff'ring parents meekly tried
To keep their offspring satisfied,
A task that was gargantuan —
It just went on and on and on.

One day into the countryside
The family went for a ride.
They'd packed the car with things to eat –
Buttered scones and luncheon meat –
And when a pretty spot they found
They spread the picnic on the ground.
Roberta (who was always rude)
Said, "Shan't eat *that* – it's horrid food."
Her parents with a weary sigh
Didn't ask the reason why,
But said instead, "Don't wander, dear,
The woods are wild, so stay right here."
Roberta, though, was never good
And wandered off into the wood.

Alas, by chance, she passed the lair
Of a large and hungry bear.
The beast (he didn't mean to hurt her)
Stuck out a paw and grabbed Roberta.
His mouth, he opened very wide
And popped the little girl inside.
Later on, he told his chums,
"The infant really wasn't yums –
Hardly sweet, a trifle tough
And there wasn't quite enough."

The Literary Lions

The literary lions assemble each month
for a splendid, wonderful, literary lunch.
And what are they given to stop them being boring?
And what are they given to stop them from snoring?
Why, those literary lions are given for luncheon
Celery, cheese and cream crackers to crunch on.

The Impresario

A walrus lived in ice and snow
Who was an impresario.
Each summer, in the month of June,
He'd get an orchestra to tune.
Seals, sat on icy floes,
Played violins and piccolos.
Whales blew the bass trombones
And reindeer played the saxophones.
The conductor was a polar bear
(He waved his baton in the air)
And birds and beasts from miles around
Came along to hear the sound.
The concerts were so well-attended
All were sorry when they ended.
And close to where the music played
A painted notice was displayed:

AUDIENCE APPLAUSE IS NICE
PLEASE, NOT TOO LOUD –
YOU'LL CRACK THE ICE.

Jim the Hippopotamus

There once was a hippo called Jim
Who was terribly terribly *thin*.
For whatever he ate
To add to his weight
It made no difference to him.

"Try bananas – they're fattening things,"
Said a bird with beautiful wings.
So Jim ate for lunch
Bunch after bunch
Of bananas, including the skins.

But still Jim is not at all fat
Though he's no longer sad about that,
For he swings through the trees
And with elegant ease
Drops in on his friends for a chat.

Teacher's Pets

Terence is slow as a garden snail,
Pete is as strong as a lion,
William Smith is wise as an owl,
And a wonderful cheetah is Brian.

The Fly

Why, oh why,
Did the housefly fly?
To be sure
It was the spider spied her.
But he caught her in his web
And bashed her on the head
And in his frying pan fried her.

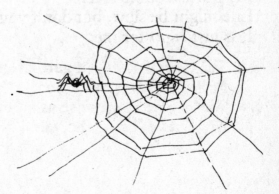

The Sloth, That's Me

I love to do just nothing,
Just nothing, all day long.
I'm lazy, very lazy,
But I ask you, what's so wrong?

The world it whizzes by outside
At a fast and dizzy pace.
What is the point, please tell me
Of that busybody race?

I love to do just nothing,
To hang about the trees,
To twiddle my toes or have a doze
And live a life of ease.

I haven't any worries,
My life is trouble-free.
Life might be slow, but don't you know
It is just *right* for me.

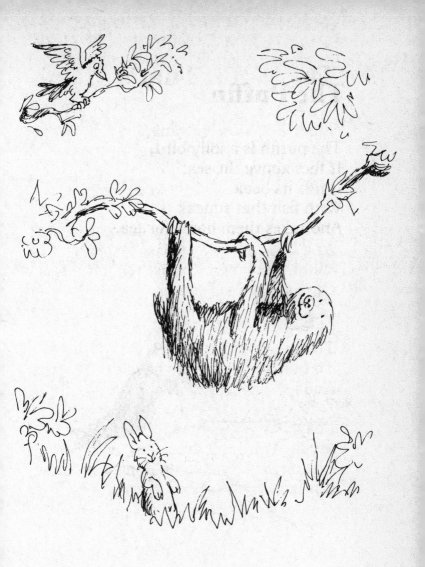

The Puffin

The puffin is a jolly bird,
It flies above the sea.
It fills its beak
With fish that squeak
And takes them home for tea.

Regina

I once met a pretty hyena,
Known by the name of Regina.
Each day she would dance
When she got the chance
And now she's a top ballerina.

Danny

Our dog Danny
Is off his food.
His dinner's untouched,
His bone's unchewed.
He doesn't want his biscuits,
He doesn't want his meat,
He doesn't want anything
Dogs usually eat.

But I think I know
(From the twinkle in his eye)
What our dog Danny
Would really like to try:
He knows what's for lunch,
He knows what's cooking –
He'd *really* like roast beef
And chocolate pudding.

Hen and Pig

A hen and a pig went for their hols
Riding in a hired Rolls.
About the countryside they drove
From Ditchling Beacon down to Hove
And then along to Beachy Head —
"Gosh, what a view!" the piggy said.
"But I think I'd better put the brake on
Or we'll end up as eggs and bacon."

Fred the Fly

Fred was a fly
Who was frightfully clever.
He could tell you the time,
He could forecast the weather.

He had read lots of books
From cover to cover
And he knew lots and lots
About something-or-other.

But the one thing Fred
Just couldn't have spotted
Was me with the paper
Before he was swotted.

The Toad

The toad is given to reflection
On the state of his complexion.
For this he is extremely fond
Of gazing often in the pond.
The creature is immensely vain
And even sits there in the rain.
And if he's feeling out of sorts
He cheers himself by counting warts.

The Ocelot

The ocelot
Has lots of spots,
He's a master of disguise.
He likes to wear dark glasses,
Waistcoats and bow ties.
He has read a lot of books
(Both little ones and large)
On Blending into Backgrounds
And the Art of Camouflage.
So he walks about the jungle
With his bow tie neatly knotted
And that clever ocelot
Is never ever spotted.

The Herring and the Whale

"How long is your tail?"
Said the herring to the whale.
"If I tell you," said the whale,
"You will laugh.
For my tale goes from me
To the Caspian Sea
And takes an hour and a half."

"Good gracious," said the fish,
"That's as long as I could wish,
I really haven't time
For any more.
You see, I have to dine
With a certain friend of mine
And it's very nearly half-past four."

"But we could go tomorrow,"
Said the whale with a swallow.
"You could travel on the tip
Of my fin.
Then you could tell your friends
You've visited both ends
And many other places in between."

The Slug

The slug he is so greedy,
He is no friend of mine.
He lives among my lettuces
On which he likes to dine.

When he's finished every one
And left a trail of slime,
He'll start upon the radishes
And eat them, one at a time.

He'll eat anything, that slug,
He thinks that that's just fine,
And, perhaps, if he's *still* hungry –
He'll even eat this rh-

Polly

Polly, while walking in the jungle,
Made a really serious bungle.
She sat right down upon a snake
And didn't realise her mistake.
All at once she felt the trees
(As it were) begin to squeeze –
A horrid, green boa constrictor,
The funny thing, it only licked her.

The Penguin

The penguin lives in Southern Seas,
He likes the colder climes.
His favourite dish
Is battered fish
With chips, wrapped in The Times.

Feeling Beastly

I'm really feeling beastly,
It's a beastly sort of day.
Everything is beastly
In a beastly sort of way.

The crododile is crying again,
It's raining cats and dogs,
The house is full of elephants,
The mice are wearing clogs.

There's a cockroach in the kitchen,
There's a spider in the bath,
There's a blockage up the chimney –
It's a forty-foot giraffe.

The horse has gone and bolted,
But left the door ajar,
And the silly geese have taken flight
In my motor car.

The bats aren't in the belfry,
The cows are all forlorn,
And the mole has made a mountain
In the middle of the lawn.

The bally ducks are grousing,
The frogs are hopping mad,
There's something fishy going on
Beneath a lily pad.

And I'd better count the chickens
For they're hatching from their shells.
It'll take a month of Sundays
And a week of wishing wells.

But I'll have to grin and bear it
And I'll find some beastly way,
And anyhow tomorrow
Is another beastly day.

MARK BURGESS

Feeling Peckish

Poems to read at mealtimes

Contents

Alphabet Soup

I just ate
An alphabet.
Did you ever
Eat a letter?
Backwards,
Forwards,
Mumbled,
Jumbled –
I've eaten a troop
In Alphabet Soup.

Good King Rowley

Good King Rowley
In his dressing gown,
Couldn't find his trousers
And couldn't find his crown.
He couldn't find his cereal,
He couldn't find his mug,
He couldn't find his milk
As he couldn't find the jug.
He couldn't find his butter-knife
And he couldn't find his bread –
So he couldn't have his breakfast
And went back to bed!

In Winter

We feed the birds
With all our scraps,
They are such hungry
Little chaps.
They wait upon the washing line
Eager for their breakfast time.
And when it's time,
The food's put out,
They squabble,
Throw the stuff about.

Such manners!
What a thing to do!
Not at all like me or you.

Crumpets

Crumpets,
Crumpets,
A word in your trumpets –
Guess how the man puts the bubbles in
Crumpets.

Well, he waits till the crumpet dough's just
    right.
(It's usually best in the middle of the night.)
Then he goes and gets the pump from his
    grandmother's bike
And he pumps and he pumps till it's bubbly
    and light.

Crumpets,
Crumpets,
Blow your own trumpets –
That's how the man puts the bubbles in
Crumpets!

Table Manners

Lack of manners was the fault
Of little Tommy Jude.
He'd always chuck about the salt
And blow upon his food.
At meals, he would never wait,
His soup he'd always slurp.
He'd spread his food around the plate,
He'd hiccup and he'd burp.
But then he had an accident,
So sad for one so young,
For as he licked his knife, it bent,
Thus cutting off his tongue.

Wellington George

Wellington George
Is as round as a ball.
He is podgy. He's plump.
He is not thin at all.
He is fond of his food,
He can't go without
And perhaps that's the reason
Why Wellington's stout.

He likes a big breakfast
And a snack at eleven.
Then luncheon at one
And dinner at seven.
And in-between times
Things to nibble and munch,
To gnaw and to chew
And to bite and to crunch.
He's fond of his food –
There's no shadow of doubt
And that's probably why
He's exceedingly stout.

But last week, an ordeal
Poor Wellington faced –
He went to the vet
Who measured his waist.

Now Wellington George
Has become rather glum
And he's trying so hard
Not to think of his tum.
No murmur of munching –
The house is all quiet –
For Wellington George
Has been put on a diet.

My Uncle Reg

My Uncle Reg
Grows lovely veg:
Marrows and beans,
Carrots and greens.
Parsnips, potatoes,
Lettuce, tomatoes,
Beetroot and radishes,
Peas and cabbages –
On his little plot
He grows the lot.

One Little Hen

One little hen, sitting by the gate,
Laid me an egg for my breakfast plate.

Two little hens, sitting by a tree,
Laid me eggs for lunch and tea.

Three little hens, sitting in the sun,
Didn't lay eggs for anyone.

Milking Time

Down among the marigolds, in the grassy
    glade,
Six brown cows sit chewing in the shade.

'Don't you think it's time, dear?'
Daisy says to Sue.
Susie says to Buttercup:
'I think so, dear, don't you?'
'I'm sure you're right,' says Buttercup.
'But Peg, do you agree?'
'Oh yes,' says Peg, 'how nice of you
To think of asking me.'
'I'm sure we should be going now,'
Says Daffodil to May.
'Why yes, of course, you're right dear –
Now, will you lead the way?'

Up amongst the dandelions, close beside the
  gate,
Six brown cows stand patiently and wait.

Picknicking

Down to the sea where the salt-breeze
   blows,
Down by the dunes where the marram grass
   grows;
Over the strand where the seagulls cry
And the breakers break on the rocks close
   by –
We go with our baskets, hand in hand,
Our sandals sink in the soft white sand,
To the place we know where the two streams
   meet
And the little grey fish swim round our feet.
Where the grasses ring with silver bells
And the tideline's scattered with tiny shells
And an old, old tree lies bleached and bare –
We like to eat our picnics there.

Apples

Apple pie,
I love to try.
Apple crumble,
I'll not grumble.
Apple snow,
I'll not say, 'No'.
Apple sauce?
Why yes, of course.

Apples, apples,
Cooked or raw,
I'll eat them all –
Right to the core.

I love to grapple
With an apple.

Something New

'Don't you *ever* try anything new?'
Said my aunt as she gave me some stew
Made from cabbage and ham
With strawberry jam
And what looked like the sole of a shoe.

To please her (and not to seem rude)
I stuck in my fork and I chewed,
But I can't say the flavour
Was one I could savour.
I would hardly describe it as food.

'Is that *really* all you can eat?'
Said Aunt as I pleaded defeat.
'I really thought you
Would like something new
And there's baked beans and custard for
    sweet.'

Dave the Dinosaur

In prehistoric times there lived
A dinosaur called Dave.
He didn't roam about and roar
As monsters should behave;
Instead he spent his time at home
And taught himself to cook –
He made up recipes himself
Or learnt them from a book.
And, of all the things he cooked,
The ones he liked the most
Were rock cakes dipped in treacle
And Stone-Age-man-on-toast.

Nuts

I'm nuts
About nuts.

Cobnuts,
Beechnuts,
Very-hard-to-reach-nuts,
High nuts,
Low nuts,
Coconuts,
And doughnuts.
Brazil nuts,
Chestnuts,
Nothing-but-the-best-nuts,
Peanuts,
Walnuts,
Absolutely *ALL* nuts!

The Duke of Bunting

His Grace the Duke of Bunting
Loved nothing more than hunting –
In the jungle, on the mountain or the plain.
And the creature he most sought,
For the trophy and the sport,
Was a lion with a long and flowing mane.

So he hunted quite a while
And with cunning and with guile
He cornered his quarry by a wall.
Then he cried, 'This is such fun!',
Squeezed the trigger of his gun –
But it gave a feeble 'pop' and that was all.

Well then, the lion, with a paw,
Knocked the duke on to the floor,
And he called him names (which hurt the
    fellow's pride).
So the duke said to his face
'Please address me as "Your Grace"'.
'But *grace* is what I'm saying,' the lion
    replied.

The Zink

A zink for a pet
Is really not wise
For, with feeding, they grow
To double their size.
And the things that they eat
Are not all that nice,
So before you decide
You'd better think twice.

Are you really prepared
To give up your time
To grub for grignottles
All covered in slime.
To hunt through the bushes
For figgots and spicks
Or to delve into mud
For jiggers and ticks.
For these are the things
A zink likes to eat
And its manners, I'm told,
Are hardly discreet –
It gobbles and gulps
And it wobbles its eyes –

A zink for a pet
Is *really* not wise.

Witches' Brew

Hubble-bubble on the stove,
The witches gather round.
They all declare there's no compare,
It's such a lovely sound.
'What is the formula?' cries one.
'I think I have forgot.'
'A spoon for each of us,' they shout.
'Then one more for the pot!'

Mandy

In our street
A girl called Mandy
Lives on sweets
And sugar candy.

But though the dentist's
Very willing
Mandy never needs a filling.

'What?' you cry,
'That strains belief.'
But then she hasn't
Any teef.

Black Jack

Black Jack was a pirate bold,
Who plundered passing ships
For gold, doubloons and pieces of eight
And he lived to ninety-six.
Each birthday he would celebrate
Amongst his merry crew
With coloured balloons and birthday cake
And crisps and jelly, too.

It's Good For You

'It is such *lovely* food,' they say.
They've no idea what's wrong.
'You'll sit there till you finish or
You'll never grow up strong.'

I've chewed and chewed,
But hate it so –
I'll have to stay the same.
In fact, I think
I would rather *SHRINK*
Than eat liver once again.

What I'd Like

I'd like chocs,
Lots and lots –
A great big chock-a-block box of chocs.

The Pudding Shop Burglary

Two burglars known as Bill and Ben
Hatched a cunning plan
To raid a pudding shop and then
Drive off in a van.

Alas for Bill and Ben, the Law
Got to know their scheme
And as the two came through the door
The Police were at the scene.

The puddings Bill and Ben had grabbed
They'd stuffed into their shirts
And so, of course, when they were nabbed
They got their just desserts.

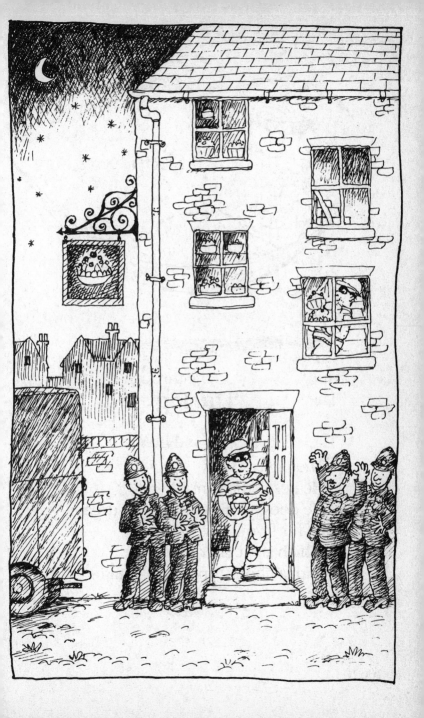

The Pig

The pig is so lazy
He lies in the sun.
He does nothing all day but dream
Of his favourite food,
Which is blueberry pie
With a liberal topping of cream.

The Lettuce

As any gardener will know,
Lettuces aren't hard to grow;
Except they have a nasty habit
Of being eaten by a passing rabbit.

Too Many Cooks In The Soup

The cooks are making minestrone.
Cyril's picked a fight with Tony.
Bert forgot to chop the onions.
Nigel trod on David's bunions.
Freddy sneezed into the mustard,
James is now all hot and flustered.
Sidney's sure it has to boil,
Matthew says it's bound to spoil.
Ronnie puts in too much salt.
Thomas says it's not his fault.
Now the manager appears,
Fuming, angry, close to tears;
Shouts at them for being so late –
How the guests have had to wait –
Surely someone saw the clock?
Now he'll be a laughing stock.

Mice

Nothing entices
Little brown mice
Like pieces of cheeses –
That easily pleases.

Trafalgar Square

Let's feed the pigeons in Trafalgar Square –
There are so many pigeons there.
For twenty pence we'll buy some seed,
Hold out our hands and watch them feed.
They're not afraid – they'll perch on us
And make an awful lot of fuss
And when they've gone we're sure to find
They've all left messages behind.

The Spangly Dragon

The spangly dragon, he flies through the air,
He hasn't a worry, he hasn't a care.
He flaps high above on his bumbly wings
And with crumbly voice he joyfully sings:

> *'I'm the spangly dragon,*
> *I'll weave you a spell,*
> *I'll tell you a fib*
> *And a story as well.*
> *I'll eat all your gumdrops,*
> *I'll drink all your fizz,*
> *I'm the spangliest dragon*
> *That ever there is.'*

On his bumbly wings he flies to the moon
And he nibbles away while humming this
    tune.
Then when he has finished, he's had his last
    bite,
The spangly dragon flies into the night.

Pancakes

Toss a pancake, if you can,
Back into the frying pan,
For pancakes stuck upon the ceiling
Really are far less appealing.

Lemon Curd

My Auntie Alice has inferred
That life depends on lemon curd
Of which the sun itself is made
(The moon, of course, is marmalade).

Nibble, Peck

Peck, peck,
Nibble, nibble,
Gnaw, gnaw,
Dribble, dribble,
Chew, chew,
Munch, munch,
Gobble, gobble,
Crunch, crunch,
Slurp, slurp,
Gulp, gulp,
Swallow, swallow,
Burp.

An Elephant Sufficiency

After dinner
I asked my guest
If with the meal
He'd been impressed.
He replied at once,
'Most certainly,
Quite delicious. It seems to me
I'm really, nearly, F. to B.*
I've had, I'm sure, quite definitely
An elegant sufficiency.'

* *Full to Bursting*

The Tuppenny Twins

When you're hungry, feeling peckish,
When you've got a rumbly tum,
Then the Tuppenny Twins will fix it
With a smile and some fun.
Just call them and they'll hurry –
They'll be there in a trice
With their cherry cakes and jellies
And their cream-and-strawberry-ice.

'We are the Tuppenny Twins,' they sing.
'We never hesitate –
Speedy sustenance we bring
And plonk it on your plate.'

They'll ride up on their tricycle
And ring upon the bell
And just in case you didn't hear
They'll honk the horn as well.
And balanced high in baskets
Or in boxes, they have brought
Caramels and custard tarts
And food of every sort.

'We are the Tuppenny Twins,' they sing.
'Purveyors of delight,
Conveyors of comestibles –
And any day or night!'

The Gumbus-goo

The gumbus-goo,
He lives on glue.
Oh, what a funny thing to do!
It's most peculiar,
He gets gluier,
Gumbus-gooier
And
Gooier!

A Man from
Weston-super-Mare

A man from Weston-super-Mare
Lived on nothing but fresh air.
He'd be living there today
If he hadn't blown away.

In Outer Space

Astronauts in outer space
Don't eat the same as us.
If they had fish and chips and peas
It would cause no end of fuss.
The chips and peas would float around
In weightless jamboree –
And astronauts would all need nets
With which to catch their tea.

The Midnight Fox

By milky moon
The midnight fox
Comes trotting into town;
With mask of white
And gold eyes bright
And coat of rusty brown.

Around the houses
Hard he seeks,
In dusky shadows steals
From rubbish bins
And empty tins
His hard-won meagre meals.

Gingerbread Man

A gingerbread man I made one day.
I made him a horse with which to play
And up he jumped and rode away,
My gingery gingerbread man.

Over the table and on to the floor –
He rode right out of the kitchen door
And that's the last I ever saw
Of my gingery gingerbread man.

Before Bed

An elephant likes cocoa
When going to bed
Which he drinks with the aid of his trunk.
But milk or hot chocolate
Are all right instead
With a couple of biscuits to dunk.

MARK BURGESS

Can't Get to Sleep

Poems to read at bedtime

Contents

CAT NAPS

There in the sun a tom cat lies
Relaxed, asleep with tight-shut eyes.
A timid mouse steps lightly past,
Glad to head for home at last.
An eye half opens, ears are pricked,
Tom cat's ginger tail is flicked –
But that is all; the mouse is gone,
Safely home and cat sleeps on.

I DON'T WANT
TO GO TO BED

I don't want to go to bed,
I'd rather stay up late instead.
I wish you weren't quite so meticulous –
Bed at eight is quite ridiculous.
With lots of time still left today
Tomorrow is so far away.
There's still so much I haven't done,
Going to bed just isn't fun.
Look at the clock – it isn't late –
I'm just not going, so bed can wait!

All right, all right, don't get cross,
I'm going now, I know who's boss.
Look, I'm nearly halfway there –
My foot is on the bottom stair.
You'll come and read? You said you would.
You'd better or I won't be good.

BATHTIME

I love a bath,
I love a bath –
It is such jolly fun.
There's nothing like
A bath for laughs,
I'm always having one.
I like to splash,
I like to splosh
In water nice and hot.
I like to wash
And wash and wash –
I love it such a lot.
And when it's over
And I'm clean
It's really such a shame,
So out I go
And play with mud –
So I can bath again!

THIS BED IS TOO SMALL

This bed is too small,
I've grown too tall.
Look, a hole in the sheet –
To make room for my feet.

NEW PYJAMAS

New pyjamas
Go bananas
Run around and shout like llamas!

New pyjarmies
Like salamis
Down our legs and up our armies!

Crisp new pyjims
Flap like pigeons
Quack like ducks and squawk like chickens!

Brand new jimjams
Just like wigwams
Yours are small and mine are a big man's!

THE HAPPY
HIGHWAYMAN

Long ago, in days of old,
When nights were very long,
There lived a happy highwayman,
The subject of this song.
His name was Thomas Turnip
And his fame had spread abroad.
The King had ordered his arrest
For thirty pence reward.

Now everywhere that Thomas went
He'd giggle and guffaw –
He'd laugh at anything at all
And roll about the floor.
He rode a fearsome horse of course,
Her name was Beastly Belle
And every joke that Thomas told,
The horse would laugh as well.

Tom rode around at dead of night
About the countryside.
He'd stop a passing coach and then
He'd take a peek inside.
Then he'd give a hearty shout,
He'd bellow loud and clear:
"Wake up, you load of nincompoops,
Did everybody hear?"

And thus he robbed them of their sleep,
These poor, well-meaning folk.
But Happy Tom would laugh and laugh,
Then tell some awful joke.
And then he'd ride away again
As quickly as he could –
Exactly why he did all this
Was never understood.

DAWN MCHORN

Dawn McHorn is always yawning,
She yawns at night and in the morning.
She yawns at breakfast, lunch and tea,
She yawns for everyone to see.
Her yawning quite obscures her features
And when at school, she yawns at teachers.
And every question they ask Dawn
She always answers with a yawn.
All are agreed, it's quite appalling –
Dawn McHorn is ALWAYS yawning.

THE BAT

The batty bat sleeps upside down,
A funny thing to do.
I've never tried that way myself –
I wonder, p'rhaps, have you?

SNOW IN THE LAMPLIGHT

From my bedroom,
In bare feet,
I look through curtains,
Down the street
To the lamp-post
There below,
Lighting up
The falling snow.
Snow like feathers
In the light,
Like some gigantic
Pillow-fight.
Will it settle?
I'm hoping so.
Drifting,
Sledging,
Snowball snow.

KITTY KITTY

Kitty Kitty sang to the moon,
Kitty Kitty sang out of tune.
Though the Moon
Did wax and wain
Kitty did not sing again.

PROFESSOR ETCETERA

Professor Etcetera's earnest and wise,
He has grey hair, glasses and little blue eyes.
He spends all his time in research and in study
And he hardly goes out to see anybody.

He's studying sleep from all different angles.
He's working with sheets, pillowcases and
    mangles.
He's testing all sorts of alarm bells and clocks
And trying on nightcaps, slippers and socks.

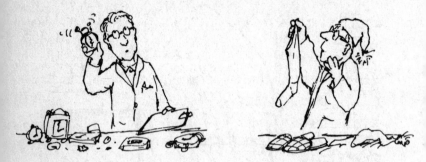

He's studying naps, forty winks and light dozes.
He's measuring snores from all sorts of noses.
He's bouncing on beds and testing their springs
And he's trying out quilts and duvets and things.

So hush, hush,
Do not disturb.
Quiet, please,
For surely you've heard?
The prof. is intent
On an experiment
AND NO ONE MUST UTTER A WORD!

COUNTING SHEEP

As I was going off to sleep
I met a shepherd with his sheep.
The shepherd called me from my slumbers
And asked if I was good at numbers.
He said he had to check his stock
And wanted me to count his flock.
I soon agreed with his request
And, counting them, I did my best:
Twenty ewes and twenty rams
And twenty little woolly lambs.
"That's right," the shepherd cried, delighted.
"I really think you should be knighted."
And off he wandered with his flock.
And then I thought I heard a clock –
And just as they all reached the farm,
"Ding-a-ling" went my alarm.

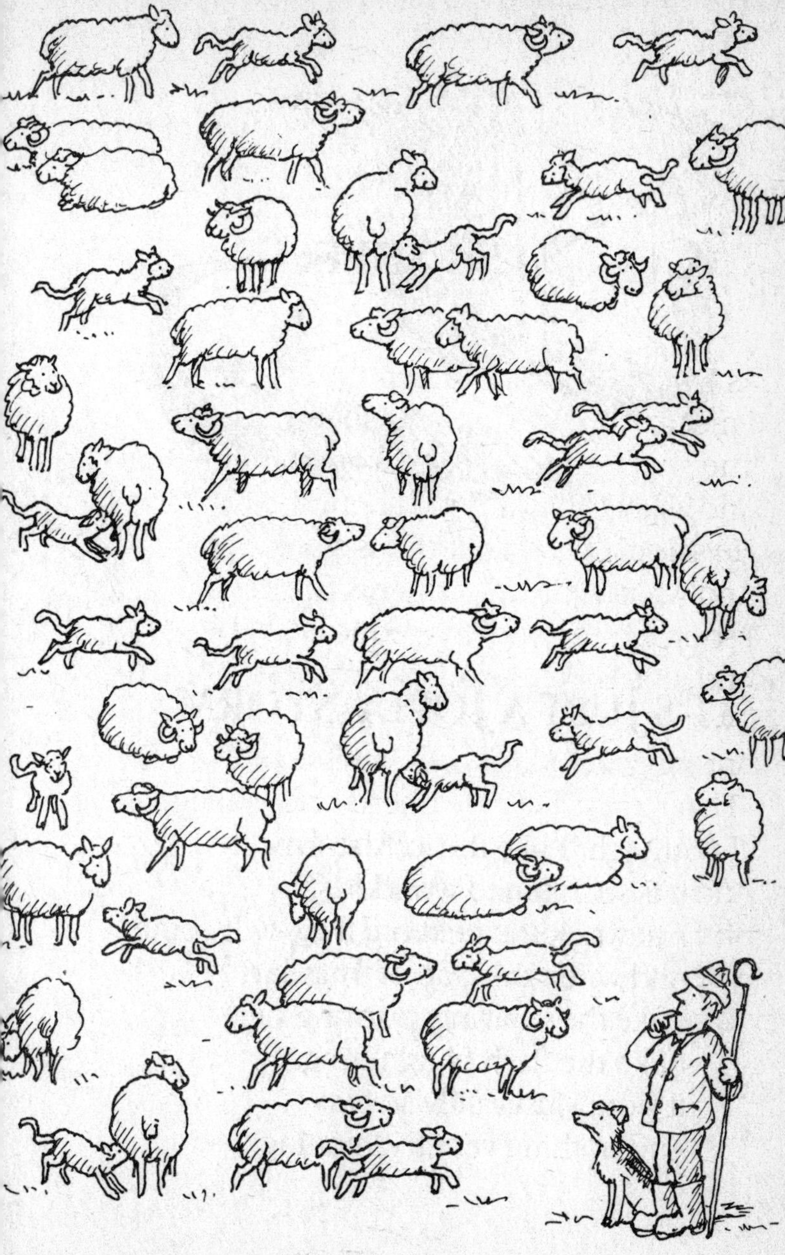

IT'S JUST A JOLLY STORM

At night I like the jolly storm,
It is such fun to wonder
Just when the next big flash will come
And when the clap of thunder.
I like the pouring, pouring rain,
I like the flash of lightning.
It's only just a silly storm –
And nothing very frightening!

GOOD KING ROWLEY

Good King Rowley,
Rowley-Powley,
Went to bed
In bedsocks (holey).
The bedsocks (royal),
Did not spoil
As Good King Rowley
Put-them-on-slow-ly.

THE OWL'S
BIRTHDAY PARTY

The Owl's Birthday Party
Is bound to be a hoot –
There's birthday cake and jelly
And coloured balloons to boot.

The bats are bringing chocolates
The squirrels, custard pies.
The birthday cake is full of worms,
The jelly's full of flies.

Everyone's invited,
We'll have a lot of fun.
The Owl really is a sport –
AND SO SAYS EVERYONE.

NOAH'S ARK

One stormy night, when all was dark,
The stormy waves beat round the Ark.
Hard on the roof the rain did fall –
Poor Noah could not sleep at all.
The noise outside was matched within,
There really was a frightful din.

Dogs barked
Warthogs called,
Bats squeaked
Cats caterwauled,
Elephants stamped
And tigers growled,
Hippos snorted
Wolves howled,
Parrots squawked
And monkeys chattered,
Donkeys brayed
And toads nattered.
But worst of all,
The rhino's snores
Shook and rattled all the doors.

Then, his cabin door flung wide,
Noah looked about and cried:
"Quiet, please – I'm all upset –
I haven't slept a wink as yet.
This awful noise has got to cease;
Please let's have a bit of peace!"

The beasts saw Noah's angry frown
And, all at once, they settled down.
Then, singing softly, they did try
To soothe him with a lullaby.
Gently into sleep he fell
And in the Ark then all was well.
Except, that is,
For *Noah's* snores
Which shook and rattled all the doors.

MIDNIGHT FEAST

I'm often hungry in the night,
I think how nice to have a bite.
So down the stairs I softly creep
While everyone is sound asleep.
And then I help myself to cheese,
A sandwich filled with mushy peas,
Or marmalade on buttered toast –
They're the things I like the most.
Then when I'm full and feel well fed
I creep upstairs and back to bed.
But in the morning, strange to tell,
At breakfast, I don't feel so well.

THE LONG-CASE CLOCK

Tick tock,
Tick tock,
Goes the long-case clock.
Standing tall
By the wall
In the main front hall.
And the rhymes
Of the chimes
Give signs of the times.
And right
In the night
At the strike of mid-night
From the base
Of the case
Peers a little grey face.

GRANDPA NEVER SLEEPS

Grandpa doesn't sleep at night,
He never sleeps a wink.
Instead he tinkers with the car
Or mends the kitchen sink.

Sometimes he picks the rhubarb
Or polishes the floor.
And other nights he's shopping
At the local all-night store.

Last night he papered half the hall
And built a garden shed.
But when the rest of us got up
He *didn't* go to bed.

I don't know how he does it,
He's always on the go.
Grandpa never sleeps AT ALL –
At least, I think that's so . . .

SANTA CLAUS GETS
THE WRONG NIGHT

One summertime, not long ago,
There was no ice, there was no snow,
But Santa, fast asleep one night,
Dreamt everywhere was snowy white.
It was (he dreamt) late in December –
A busy time for him, remember.

All of a sudden he awoke,
He grabbed his hat, he grabbed his cloak.
He stuffed some presents in his sack
And lifted it upon his back.
He called his reindeer, found his sleigh,
He harnessed them without delay
And then he urged them swiftly fly
Up into the starlit sky.

Soon after this they reach a house.
They landed, softly as a mouse
And Santa, with his bulging sack,
Headed for the chimney-stack.
Down the chimney he did go
And came out in the room below.
But then, his foot still on the grate,
Something made him hesitate.
The room was bare –
No decorations?
No Christmas greetings from relations?
No brightly coloured Christmas tree?
All this puzzled Mr C.
And worst of all – extremely shocking –
Nowhere could he find a stocking.

Then, all at once, there caught his eye
A calendar. The month: July.
Like lightning Santa saw his blunder.
Why, he didn't stop to wonder,
But needing no additional proof,
He dashed back up on to the roof.
He urged his reindeer to make haste –
Back across the sky they raced
And just before the hour of dawn
They landed on his own front lawn.
Santa went straight back to bed,
An awful throbbing in his head
And only later did he find
He'd left his Christmas sack behind.

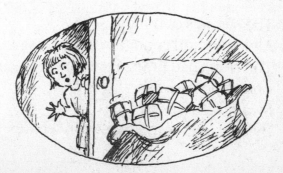

SWEET DREAMS

Last night my dreams
Were of peppermint creams,
Of sherbet and coconut ice;
Of turkish delight
All ready to bite,
Of toffee and pink sugar mice.

The sky was all spangles
And candifloss tangles,
The moon was a bright lollipop.
Each hill was of candy
And flavoured with brandy
With a dollop of cream on the top.

The sea was of honey,
All lovely and runny –
The ships had liquorice sails.
And chocolate fish
Swam with a swish
By the sides of the marzipan whales.

THE CUCUMBER TREE

The cucumber tree
Is a wonder to see,
It's a beautiful sight in the spring –
When birds of a feather
All gather together
Each morning and evening to sing.

But the greatest of wonders
Is the crop of cucumbers –
Each one has a luminous glow.
And monkeys pick bunches
To brighten their lunches
And see their way home in the snow.

While back on the land
By the soft sugar sand
Peppermint horses all pranced.
And bells of meringue
Cheerfully rang
As off to the morning I danced.

THE PIGEONS ALL HAVE HOBNAIL BOOTS

The pigeons all have hobnail boots,
They dance with heavy tread.
All through the night they're on the tiles –
I hear them from my bed.

Perhaps they think they're Nureyev
Or maybe Fred Astaire,
But anyway I wish they'd go
And dance about elsewhere.

THE BADGER

Brock, Brock,
It's ten o'clock,
Time for your evening wander.
Through moonlight pace
With stripy face,
To woodlands over yonder.

But Brock, Brock,
At five o'clock,
End your night-time ramble.
Turn your tread
Towards your bed
Beneath the tangled bramble.

TWILIGHT IN THE PARK

It is twilight in the park
And the dogs begin to bark,
On their early evening walks they are bound.
So pug, poodle and Dalmatian,
Corgi, spaniel and Alsatian,
Together, they all love to run around.

For there's nothing like the gloaming
For a bit of canine roaming,
To meet and catch up on the latest news.
To sniff and pick at bones
Then be off back to their homes
To baskets by the fire and a snooze.

THE GREAT BED
OF WARE

Oh, there's none to compare
With the Great Bed of Ware.
It's so great
And ornate,
It's eleven foot square.
A delight,
It is right
At the top of the stair
And there's always
Plenty of room to spare.

It once slept a knight
And his horse and his squire,
A maid and her aunt
And a parish church choir,

A king and a queen
In their courtly attire,
And a butcher and baker
And wandering friar,

A blacksmith with coals
Still hot from his fire,
A gooseboy with geese
And the local Town Crier,

A cat and a mouse
And a hat-pin supplier
And a newly-wed couple
They all did admire.

For there's none to compare
With the Great Bed of Ware.
There's normally
Plenty of room to spare,
But that night
It fell right
To the foot of the stair
With a crash.
Now, alas,
It is under repair.

CAN'T GET TO SLEEP?

I can't get to sleep,
I've counted sheep –
It hasn't worked of course.
No forty winks,
Instead I think
Of mutton and mint sauce.

No better are pigs
All dancing jigs,
Or running through the woods.
Much worse are girls
With golden curls
And bright-red riding hoods.

I've counted flowers
For hours and hours,
I thought they'd do the trick –
But no such luck.
I'm really stuck
For something, please and quick.

I've closed my eyes,
I've tried and tried,
It's awful, I could weep –
I'm wide awake
For goodness sake –
I NEED MY BEAUTY SLEEP!

BEDTIME STORY

Now listen, child, before you sleep,
To this improving tale –
It's bound to make you grow up good,
I've never known it fail.
Have you finished fidgeting?
For if you have, then I'll begin.

There lived a girl, not long ago,
Her parents called her Jenny.
Her manners were the best in town
And talents, she had many.
What is it now? I thought I said
To bring some water up to bed.

Jenny loved to work and work.
She loved to go to school.
She always learnt her lessons well
And never broke a rule.
Goodness gracious, what is wrong?
Just settle down – Shall I go on?

Now Jenny met a lion one day,
But she knew what to do.
For Jenny, boldly, said to him:
'I'm not afraid of you.'
You have to go? Oh, surely not.
I think you'll like this bit a lot.

The lion really was impressed –
It went all meek and mild.
Such are the powers of a good,
Polite, well-mannered child.
I'll read some more? Just for a treat . . .?
How very odd, you've gone to sleep.

STARS

Up above, the stars are twinkling,
Hundreds, thousands,
Quite a sprinkling.
Just how many?
I've no inkling,
That's what little me is thinkling.

LETTER FROM THE LAND OF NOD

Dear Sir,

From our records, it seems
That, last night, when you called in your dreams,
You left behind proof
That you'd just lost a tooth
In the place where your pillow had been.

But then, it appears, you forgot
To claim your reward, which is odd.
So as due recompense
We enclose twenty pence.

Yours truly,

The Fairies of Nod.

IF I WERE A DORMOUSE

If I were a dormouse
I'd have a little warm house.
For I'd be sure to choose
Somewhere comfortable to snooze.
My bed would be just right
For a dreamy, sleepy night.
And if you should take a peep
I'd be sure to be asleep.

IN BED

Now we're ready,
Me and teddy.
Into bed
Our "Goodnights" said.
Night night,
Sleep tight,
Turn out the light.

Bed's the place I like to be –
Especially when my ted's with me.